Bella has set up a food shop in the shed.

She has bananas, eggs,
pasta and bags of crisps.

Tom goes into Bella's shop.

'Hello, Tom,' she says.

‘Please may I have a bag of crisps?’ he says to Bella.

Bella gets a bag of crisps for Tom.

‘That will be 20p,’ she says.

But Tom has no money.

‘I will lend you 20p,’ says Bella. She gets 20p from the till.

Tom pays Bella 20p. He is happy. Bella is not happy.